Multiplication Rules!

An **Activity Book** of times tables

by Penny Topsom
illustrated by Rosie Brooks

rbp
Ragged Bears Publishing

First published and distributed in the United Kingdom in 2009 by Ragged Bears Publishing Ltd,
14A Bennetts Field IE, Southgate Road, Wincanton, Somerset BA9 9DT.

Tel: 01963 34300 orders@raggedbears.co.uk www.raggedbears.co.uk

A CIP record of this book is available from the British Library

ISBN 978-1-85714-398-0

Printed in Poland

Contents

Foreword

These grids came about when Harvey, one of my sons, asked me a simple question. Faced with learning his times tables, he asked, 'Where's the table?'

'This is the table,' I replied, pointing to the list.

'It doesn't look like a table to me,' he said. 'Can we draw one?'

So I drew a rectangular shape, like the table we were sitting at. As we were learning his two times table, he wrote 1 x 2 = 2, 2 x 2 = 4, and so on, inside the rectangle. He found this quite fun, but soon we were running out of space and he was running out of steam. So I suggested that to keep the numbers separate, we should divide our rectangular table shape into smaller boxes. To make it even simpler, I said he could just put the answer numbers (2, 4, 6 etc) into each separate box. Our rectangle shape was big enough for 15 boxes (3 rows of 5).

It looked a bit like a map with grid references, so we decided to call it our times table grid.

Instead of the usual tension that accompanied the learning of times tables, Harvey was starting to treat it like a game; as he said each one, e.g. '1 times 2 is …', he would point to the box where he'd written his answer. By covering certain boxes and asking him questions such as '2 times 2 equals what?', I could turn it into a memory game, and he began to remember not only the answer number, but also where the answer box was situated on the grid.

This was all well and good for Harvey, but would the same approach work with Sonny? Our eldest son, like myself, has severe dyslexia and found maths particularly challenging. When I was at school I'd spend half the maths lessons looking like a startled rabbit and the other half trying to become invisible. The endless numbers in the times table lists pinned on the classroom wall would just start to blur, together with the big 'Multiplication Square' (10 boxes along and 10 boxes down, 100 boxes in all, with times tables running down in columns). There was simply too much information for me to take in.

Armed with confidence and a blank sheet of paper, I drew another rectangular times table grid, explaining that we were going to try learning times tables in a slightly different way. He watched with amusement, mainly due to the amount of boxes that were being drawn, but if his younger brother could do it then he certainly could. (Sibling rivalry can come in handy sometimes!)

I explained to him that we were going to place an answer number in each square in the grid. To keep the answer numbers in order, I numbered the boxes from 1 to 15 as shown below:

1	2	3	4	5
6	7	8	9	10
11	12	13	14	15

Now that I had removed all of the symbols (x and =) and the repeated times table number, Sonny was able to concentrate on the answer numbers, and he took up the challenge. As he chanted the traditional times table 'mantra' ('1 times 2 is 2', '2 times 2 is 4' etc), he filled in just the answer numbers, starting in box 1 and working his way along each row. By looking at the completed times table grid, and with repeated practice, he began to see — and consequently learn — the times table number sequence much more easily.

The boys have now used this method of learning for a number of years, working through each table as they were asked to learn them. These patterns have since become a handy memory tool, as the moaning stopped, the 'maths fog' slowly began to lift, and we started to see exciting number patterns that helped us learn each times table visually.

If these times table grids can help put a stop to confused faces, crying or good old-fashioned sulking, you never know — maths may even start to become enjoyable!

2	4	6	8	10
1	2	3	4	5
12	14	16	18	20
6	7	8	9	10
22	24	26	28	30
11	12	13	14	15

Introduction

In the 5th Century AD a clever old Roman called Victorius of Aquitaine sat down one night and worked out a vast multiplication table, a massive 98 columns along and 50 down! Thankfully we only have to learn the first 12 columns; personally I think we've got off lightly. Imagine: in his day, if we didn't know our times tables well enough, we could have been entered into a gladiatorial fight!

Multiplication means adding the same number over and over again, but to avoid confusion, the + symbol has been tipped over to make an x symbol. Multiplication is a 'short cut'; for example, with the sum 2 x 6, the first number (2) tells us to count the second number (6) twice. Thank goodness Victorius sat down and worked this out for us instead of going out that night, otherwise we could still be writing 98 + 98 + 98 + 98 + 98 (and so on), fifty times, instead of just 98 x 50! So thank you, Victorius! (Incidentally, 98 x 50 = 4,900.)

Despite Victorius' hard work we still need to find ways of learning and remembering those times table lists. By 'spring cleaning' - taking out the repeated symbols and numbers and placing the answer numbers in a small manageable grid - you can then learn the lists visually. With less clutter to distract your eye, the numbers won't feel like they're 'ganging up' on you; you (and your child) will be able to see that they are actually there to help you. Also, saying the times tables out loud, e.g. '1 times 3 is 3, 2 times 3 is 6', etc, goes well with this visual method of learning. With practice and repetition, by saying them out loud whilst looking or writing them down, they should be retained in your short-term memory. If you then go back and practise this same approach a week, a month, or even six months later, they should find their way into your long-term memory, where they could stay forever! In the lessons this learning method is referred to in two different ways:

look, say, practise

and **cover, say, practise.**

You will see that I have broken down the times table grids into three rows of five boxes.

By learning one row at a time, the times tables can be built up gradually, at a pace that suits you or your child. Do not move on to a new row until you are completely confident with the preceding one.

Top Row

2	4	6	8	10
1	2	3	4	5

Middle Row

12	14	16	18	20
6	7	8	9	10

Bottom Row

22	24	26	28	30
11	12	13	14	15

Throughout the book I will be using two phrases to describe patterns which will help you to learn and remember your grids. The first is the **follow-down pattern**, which works with your even times tables, and then there's the **jump-down pattern**, which works with those slightly tricky odd times tables. I will explain how these patterns work when we first meet them. Being able to identify odd and even numbers will help you recognise and use these patterns, so they are dealt with in the first lesson.

Difficulties in writing can hamper some people's learning, so there are cut-out **answer numbers** for use with the blank **working grids**. As you might already have noticed, my times table grids ask you to work up to 15, not the traditional 10 or 12. Before you panic, close this book or run – don't worry! All the answer numbers are ready for you to use, right up to 15 x 12 = 180 (bull's-eye!).

Once you understand how the times table grids work and are confident with them, you will find a lesson showing how they can be used to work out basic division. At the end of the book there are some simple games which will help you find out how well you or your child has remembered the times tables (not that I suggest you play any of these games at children's parties - you may not make yourself popular!).

When revising or in a test situation, times table grids can be drawn almost like a doodle, numbered and filled in by hand. Sonny is now using the grids to help him work out more complicated maths formulas (long multiplication, ratio, fractions and factors, etc).

The best way to learn times tables is to try to keep things light and fun, and not to work for longer than say twenty minutes at a time. Repetition is the key to success.

Lesson One – Getting Started

The Times Table Grid

Top Row				
Middle Row				
Bottom Row				

For each times table you are learning, work on the top row first until confident with all the numbers, then move on to the middle row. Only move on to the bottom row when you are confident with all the numbers on the top and middle rows. In this way the times table grid can be built up gradually.

At the back of this book you will find a tear-out working grid; the boxes are numbered from 1 to 15. We will use the working grid throughout this book for practice. Have a look at the box numbers on the working grid until you are familiar with the positions of each box within the grid, then put it away.

Activity 1: Test yourself with THE GRID GAME

- On the empty times table grid on the left, point to each box and call its number out loud, work from left to right. (This is useful to do as it will make you more familiar with the box sequence and the layout of the grid.)

- How fast can you point to the box when someone calls out the box number? (e.g. 'BOX 1' – point to the first box).

- Practise doodling on and numbering these grids, to the point where you are so familiar with the shape and the box numbers that you start to see them in your mind's eye.

Odds and evens

In order to work with the times table patterns, we will need to be able to recognise odd and even numbers.

For instance: Does your house or flat have an odd or even number?
How about your birthday?
Is your age odd or even?

Activity 2: Odds and evens

Use the working grid from the back of the book.

✂ Cut out the odd and even cards from page 49.

Look at the small box numbers on the working grid. Decide whether to place an odd or an even card in each box.
(For example, is 2 an odd or even number? If you think it's an even number put an 'even' card in the box.)

- How many even numbers are there between boxes 1 and 5?

_____

- How many odd numbers are there all together on the grid?

_____

- Are there more odd or more even numbers on the grid?

_____

Let's test this out with some big numbers on the bottom rows of some times table grids you will come across later on.

Top Tip!

When dealing with double numbers like 81, or bigger numbers like 398, we always look at the last digit ('digit' = posh maths word for 'number'!) to help us.

So 81 is an odd number (because 1 is an odd number)

and 398 is an even number (8 is even).

We will discover lots of odd and even patterns in our times table grids.

Let's test this out with some big numbers on the bottom rows of some times table grids you will come across later on.

- Place an 'odd' or 'even' card under each box on each row, this time looking at the big answer numbers in each box.

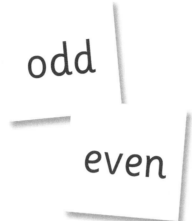

Bottom Row
(2 times table)

22	24	26	28	30
11	12	13	14	15
'odd' or 'even'	'odd' or 'even'	'odd' or 'even'	'odd' or 'even'	'odd' or 'even'

Bottom Row
(8 times table)

88	96	140	112	120
11	12	13	14	15
'odd' or 'even'	'odd' or 'even'	'odd' or 'even'	'odd' or 'even'	'odd' or 'even'

Bottom Row (12 times table)	132	144	156	168	180
	11	12	13	14	15
	'odd' or 'even'	'odd' or 'even'	'odd' or 'even'	'odd' or 'even'	'odd' or 'even'

even

- Have you been using the same type of card (i.e. odd one or even ones) over and over again?

- That's right; all the answer numbers above are even.

You will see this 'even pattern' in the 2, 4, 6, 8, 10 and 12 times tables.

Let's try three more:

- Again, place an 'odd' or 'even' card under each box on each row, still looking at the big answer numbers.

Bottom Row
(3 times table)

33	36	39	42	45
11	12	13	14	15
'odd' or 'even'	'odd' or 'even'	'odd' or 'even'	'odd' or 'even'	'odd' or 'even'

Bottom Row
(7 times table)

77	84	91	98	105
11	12	13	14	15
'odd' or 'even'	'odd' or 'even'	'odd' or 'even'	'odd' or 'even'	'odd' or 'even'

Bottom Row (11 times table)	121	132	143	154	165
	11	12	13	14	15
	'odd' or 'even'	'odd' or 'even'	'odd' or 'even'	'odd' or 'even'	'odd' or 'even'

- Did you use all odd cards this time?

- No? Was there a pattern to the order in which you put the cards down?

- That's right; they keep going 'odd', 'even', 'odd', 'even', again and again!

You will see this 'odd-even-odd' pattern in the 3, 5, 7, 9, and 11 times tables.

Lesson Two – 2 Times Table

Top Row	2 1	4 2	6 3	8 4	10 5
Middle Row	12 6	14 7	16 8	18 9	20 10
Bottom Row	22 11	24 12	26 13	28 14	30 15

Introducing . . . the 'FOLLOW-DOWN' pattern.

Take a look at the last digits of the answer numbers in each box of the top row above; do these numbers 'follow down' to the answer numbers in the boxes below?

Let's take box 4 as an example: the digit 8 'follows down' to box 9 (answer number 18). Does it also 'follow down' into box 14? Yes, the answer number here is 28. So 8 has 'followed down' all the way from the top to the bottom row.

All of the numbers 2, 4, 6, 8 and 0 on the top row 'follow down' all the way to the bottom row and this should help you as the numbers become bigger and more complicated.

You can use the 'even' and 'follow-down' patterns with the 2, 4, 6, 8, 10 and 12 times tables! FANTASTIC!

For this and subsequent lessons we will work with cut-out numbers to aid visual learning, so put your pencils away! For this lesson you will need the numbers for the 2 times table. As we discovered in the previous lesson, the numbers in the 2 times table are all even numbers.

Cut out numbers 2, 4, 6, 8 and 10.

TOP ROW – Match them over the answer numbers on the top row of the opposite page, saying each number out loud. You can then repeat the sequence with your times table mantra: '1 times 2 is 2', '2 times 2 is 4' etc.
Look, say, practise - until you're ready to move on to the middle row.

Cut out numbers 12, 14, 16, 18 and 20.

MIDDLE ROW – Match them over the answer numbers on the middle row of the opposite page. Notice the numbers in the box above; do they both end with the same number? (This is how you use the follow-down pattern).
Remember your mantra! '6 times 2 is 12', '7 times 2 is 14' etc.
Again **look, say, practise** – until ready to move on to the bottom row.

Cut out numbers 22, 24, 26, 28 and 30.

BOTTOM ROW – Match them over the answer numbers on the bottom row of the opposite page. Again, notice the numbers in the two boxes above each number; do they both end with the same number? Can you see how the **'follow-down'** pattern has worked for you on both the middle and bottom rows?
Look, say, practise with your mantra: '11 times 2 is 22', '12 times 2 is 24' etc.

Okay – feeling confident? Let's test your visual memory.

Use the working grid to cover the practice page you have just been working on, and see if you can put the cut-out numbers in their correct boxes. **Cover, say, practise** until you feel confident with this times table.

Too easy?
Turn each number face down, pick up any number at random, then see if you can put it in its correct box.

Still too easy?
Find that pencil, see if you can draw a grid, and then write each answer in!

Only another ten times tables to go – well done!

Lesson Three – 3 Times Table

Top Row	3	6	9	12	15
	1	2	3	4	5
Middle Row	18	21	24	27	30
	6	7	8	9	10
Bottom Row	33	36	39	42	45
	11	12	13	14	15

Introducing ... the 'JUMP-DOWN' pattern

Take a look at the last digits of the answer numbers in each box on the top row above.

9

Do these numbers 'follow down' to the boxes below? No, but they do 'jump down' to the boxes in the bottom row.

24

Let's take box 3 as an example: the digit 9 doesn't 'follow down' to box 8 (answer number 24) but it does 'jump down' into box 13 (answer number 39). So the number 9 has 'jumped down' from the top row to the bottom.

39

All of the numbers 3, 6, 9, 2 and 5 on the top row 'jump down' to the bottom row. This could help you on the last row of an odd-numbered times table where the numbers get bigger and more complicated. You can use the 'odd-even-odd' and 'jump-down' patterns with the 3, 5, 7, 9 and 11 times tables! But you will need to spend more time practising the middle row.

In this lesson you will be working with threes. As 3 is an odd number, your answers will be following an 'odd-even-odd' pattern. These tables can be more tricky, especially the middle row. Look for the numbers that 'jump down' from the top to the bottom row.

Cut out numbers 3, 6, 9, 12 and 15.

TOP ROW – Match them over the answer numbers on the top row of the opposite page, saying each number out loud. You can then repeat the sequence using your times table mantra: '1 times 3 is 3', '2 times 3 is 6' etc.
Look, say, practise - until you're ready to move on to the middle row.

Cut out numbers 18, 21, 24, 27 and 30.

MIDDLE ROW – Match them over the answer numbers on the middle row of the opposite page. Remember your mantra! '6 times 3 is 18', '7 times 3 is 21' etc.
Again, **look, say, practise** – until you're ready to move on to the bottom row.

Cut out numbers 33, 36, 39, 42 and 45.

BOTTOM ROW – Match them over the answer numbers on the bottom row of the opposite page. Notice the numbers in the top row; do they both end with the same number? Can you see how the 3, 6, 9, 2 and 5 have 'jumped down' (like 'stunt numbers') from the top to the bottom row. This is the 'jump-down' pattern at work. **Look, say, practise** with your mantra: '11 times 3 is 33', '12 times 3 is 36' etc.

Visual Memory Test

Now it's time to test your visual memory.

Use the working grid to cover the practice page you have just been working on, and see if you can put the cut-out numbers into their correct boxes. **Cover, say, practise** until you feel confident with this times table.

Your challenge is to put in the correct answer number for box 8, without looking at the practice page.

Top Tip!

The odd answer numbers all sit in the odd-numbered boxes, e.g. box 1 houses answer number 3. The even answer numbers all

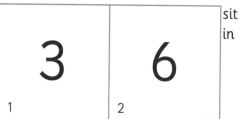

sit in

3	6
1	2

the even-numbered boxes, e.g. box 2 houses answer number 4.

Lesson Four – 4 Times Table

Top Row	4 1	8 2	12 3	16 4	20 5
Middle Row	24 6	28 7	32 8	36 9	40 10
Bottom Row	44 11	48 12	52 13	56 14	60 15

Top Tip!

Notice the link between the numbers in box 10 and box 1.

Box 10 always adds a 0 to the times table number, an easy one to remember.

Close your eyes and imagine you can see the times table grid in front of you. Can you see all 15 boxes? (Don't worry about filling it in yet!)

Here's your first chance to practise the '**follow-down**' pattern, using the 4 times table. (Recap: 'follow-down' means that you can copy the last number down from the row above, plus all the answer numbers in this times table are going to be even.)

Cut out numbers 4, 8, 12, 16 and 20.

TOP ROW – Match them over the answer numbers in the top row of the opposite page, saying each number out loud. You can then repeat the sequence with your times table mantra: '1 times 4 is 4', '2 times 4 is 8', etc.
Look, say, practise - until you're ready to move on to the middle row.

Cut out numbers 24, 28, 32, 36 and 40.

MIDDLE ROW – Match them over the answer numbers in the middle row of the opposite page. Remember the 'follow-down' pattern from the boxes above.
Mantra! '6 times 4 is 24', '7 times 4 is 28', etc.
Look, say, practise – until you are ready to move on to the bottom row.

Cut out numbers 44, 48, 52, 56 and 60.

BOTTOM ROW – Match them over the answer numbers in the bottom row of the opposite page. Notice the 'follow-down' pattern from the top and middle rows.
Look, say, practise with your mantra'
'11 times 4 is 44', '12 times 4 is 48' etc.

Visual Memory Test

Use the working grid to cover the practice page you have just been working on, and see if you can put the cut-out numbers in their correct boxes.

Cover, say, practise until you feel confident with this times table. Then shuffle the numbers and place them in their correct boxes as you turn them over.

Revision
Draw your own times table grids. Don't worry if they go wobbly, it adds to the fun! Don't just practise on paper – you could use steamed-up windows, sandy beaches or straws, pipe-cleaners, or even spaghetti (cooked or otherwise). Experiment! It all helps.

Lesson Five – 5 Times Table

Top Row	5 ₁	10 ₂	15 ₃	20 ₄	25 ₅
Middle Row	30 ₆	35 ₇	40 ₈	45 ₉	50 ₁₀
Bottom Row	55 ₁₁	60 ₁₂	65 ₁₃	70 ₁₄	75 ₁₅

Top Tip!

You could sing these; how about singing them in a rock, rap or opera style, or maybe the blues! Let's see if singing the times table grids can help us.

(Remember, box 1 tells us which times table we are working on).

Start with box 1 and sing, '1 times 5 is 5' ($1 \times 5 = 5$).

For box 2 sing, '2 times 5 is 10' ($2 \times 5 = 10$) ... and so on.

Keep going for as long as you want... or until you're told to stop!

Here's a nice simple one. **This one has an easy pattern that keeps repeating itself: 5s and 0s**. We also have the '**odd-even-odd**' pattern.

This times table also gives us a chance to practise the '**jump-down**' pattern that we learned in Lesson Three (remember, 5 is an odd number).

Cut out numbers 5, 10, 15, 20 and 25.

TOP ROW – Match them over the answer numbers on the top row of the opposite page, singing each number out loud. You can then repeat the sequence with your singing times table mantra: '1 times 5 is 5', '2 times 5 is 10', etc.
Look, say, practise - until you're ready to move on to the middle row.

Cut out numbers 30, 35, 40, 45 and 50.

MIDDLE ROW – Match them over the answer numbers on the middle row of the opposite page. (This is the only odd times table with a middle row that is easy to remember.) Sing loud and proud! '6 times 5 is 30', '7 times 5 is 35', etc.
Look, say, practise – until ready to move on to the bottom row.

Cut out numbers 55, 60, 65, 70 and 75.

BOTTOM ROW – Match them over the answer numbers on the bottom row of the opposite page. Notice the numbers in the top row, did you see them jump-down?
Look, say, practise - Sing; '11 times 5 is 55', '12 times 5 is 60', etc.

Visual Memory Test

Use the working grid to cover the practice page you have just been working on, pull your cut-out numbers out of a sock and see if you can put the numbers in their correct boxes. **Cover, say, practise** until you feel confident with this times table.

Was the order the same for your left and right sock?

Sing your answers in the style you chose earlier – or a new one, if you fancy!

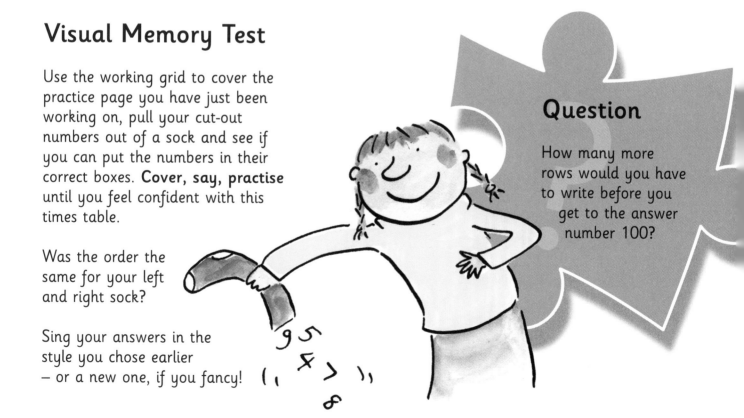

Question

How many more rows would you have to write before you get to the answer number 100?

Lesson Six – 6 Times Table

Top Row	6 ₁	12 ₂	18 ₃	24 ₄	30 ₅
Middle Row	36 ₆	42 ₇	48 ₈	54 ₉	60 ₁₀
Bottom Row	66 ₁₁	72 ₁₂	78 ₁₃	84 ₁₄	90 ₁₅

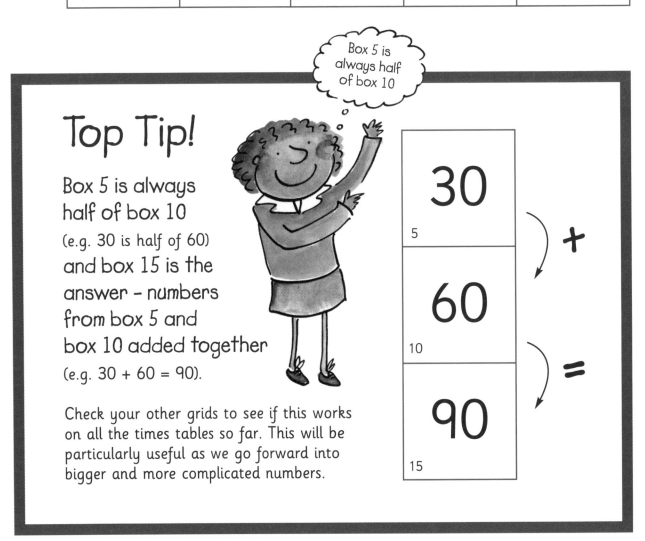

Box 5 is always half of box 10

Top Tip!

Box 5 is always half of box 10 (e.g. 30 is half of 60) and box 15 is the answer – numbers from box 5 and box 10 added together (e.g. 30 + 60 = 90).

Check your other grids to see if this works on all the times tables so far. This will be particularly useful as we go forward into bigger and more complicated numbers.

30   5
+
60   10
=
90   15

You're halfway there! Beware, from here on the numbers will now start to get bigger, even the ones along the top row. However, if we use '**follow-down**' or '**jump-down**' and our **odd-even patterns**, this shouldn't be too difficult. 6 is an even times table, so we can use ... which two patterns?

Yes, the '**follow-down**' and '**even**' patterns.

✂ Cut out numbers 6, 12, 18, 24 and 30.

TOP ROW – Match them over the answer numbers on the top row of the opposite page, saying each number out loud. You can then repeat the sequence by shouting the numbers as loud as you can in your head: '1 times 6 is 6', '2 times 6 is 12', etc (no noise should be coming from your mouth, but it will feel great! **Look, say, practise** - until you're ready to move on to the middle row.

Cut out numbers 36, 42, 48, 54 and 60.

MIDDLE ROW – Match them over the answer numbers on the middle row of the opposite page. Here comes the 'follow-down' pattern from the boxes above ... 'Head shout' (no noise!): '6 times 6 is 36', '7 times 6 is 42', etc.
Look, say, practise – until you're ready to move on to the bottom row.

Cut out numbers 66, 72, 78, 84 and 90.

BOTTOM ROW – Match them over the answer numbers on the bottom row of the opposite page. We're getting some large numbers now, but they're all still even, and they 'follow down' from the top and middle rows. **Look, say, practise** with your head-shout mantra: '11 times 6 is 66', '12 times 6 is 72', etc.

Visual Memory Test

Use the working grid to cover the practice page you have just been working on, and see if you can put the cut-out numbers in their correct boxes. **Cover, say, practise** until you feel confident with this times table.

Time yourself to see how long it takes you to fill in the grid after you've mixed the numbers up. Keep trying to beat your best score!

Revision
Practise shouting your 6 times table loudly in your head. (Don't give yourself a headache!)

Lesson Seven – 7 Times Table

Top Row	7 1	14 2	21 3	28 4	35 5
Middle Row	42 6	49 7	56 8	63 9	70 10
Bottom Row	77 11	84 12	91 13	98 14	105 15

Top Tip!

The trick is to make friends with those awkward numbers. Don't dislike 7 x 7, it's not their fault! (In fact, some people say that 7 is a lucky number!)

Once you've got to know them and their strange ways, they could be your friends for life. (7 x 7 is 49, by the way).

Slightly tricky, this one, and it might take a little longer to learn. 7 is an odd times table, so remember: our answer numbers will follow the 'odd-even-odd' pattern and the 'jump-down' pattern will be especially helpful for the bottom row.

Cut out numbers 7, 14, 21, 28 and 35.

TOP ROW – Match them over the answer numbers in the top row of the opposite page, saying each number out loud. You can then repeat the sequence. **Look, say, practise** - until you're ready to move on to the middle row.

Cut out numbers 42, 49, 56, 63 and 70.

MIDDLE ROW – Match them over the answer numbers in the middle row of the opposite page. There's no way round it, boxes 6-9 just have to become your friends! (See this lesson's Top Tip.) **Look, say, practise** – until you're ready to move on to the bottom row.

Cut out numbers 77, 84, 91, 98 and 105.

BOTTOM ROW – Match them over the answer numbers in the bottom row of the opposite page. Your 'stunt numbers' will have jumped down from the top row – thank goodness, as we've just hit our first three-digit number! **Look, say, practise** - say, '11 times 7 is 77', '12 times 7 is 84' etc.

Visual Memory Test

Use the working grid to cover the practice page you have just been working on, and see if you can put your cut-out number friends in their correct boxes.

Cover, say, practise until you feel confident with this times table.

Close your eyes and try to visualize your 7 times table, one row at a time, in your head. You can even imagine 'dropping' the answers in.

Practice

Practise visualising other times tables. (You can drift off into space with purpose now!)

Also practise seeing the grids in your head. Phew! That's what I call a brain workout!

Lesson Eight – 8 Times Table

Top Row	8 ¹	16 ²	24 ³	32 ⁴	40 ⁵
Middle Row	48 ⁶	56 ⁷	64 ⁸	72 ⁹	80 ¹⁰
Bottom Row	88 ¹¹	96 ¹²	104 ¹³	112 ¹⁴	120 ¹⁵

Top Tip!

When you're saying your times tables you may decide you just want to say the answer numbers, and why not? – so here's a little tip that may stop you from getting in a muddle. Starting with either your left or right hand you can use your fingers to keep a tally; the first hand can be used for the top row, the second hand for the middle row and then back to the first hand, this time for the bottom row. Personally, the little finger of my left hand is the fifth box; the little finger of my right hand is the tenth box, so I use my left hand twice.

(If you have trouble remembering lefts from rights, try holding up your hands palms down with thumbs pointing towards each other. The one that makes an 'L' shape is your left hand).

Have you ever considered that the 8 times table could be quite easy?

Well, we know, because 8 is even, that all the answer numbers will be even, so we use the 'follow-down' pattern.

Cut out numbers 8, 16, 24, 32 and 40.

TOP ROW – Match them over the answer numbers on the opposite page, saying each one out loud; you can then repeat the sequence.
Look, say, practise - until you're ready to move on to the middle row.

Cut out numbers 48, 56, 64, 72 and 80.

MIDDLE ROW – Match them over the answer numbers on the opposite page, saying each one out loud. If you want to just say the answer numbers then you can follow the top tip to make it easier. Repeat the sequence.
Look, say, practise, using the 'follow-down' pattern from the top row, until you're ready to move on to the bottom row.

Cut out numbers 88, 96, 104, 112 and 120.

BOTTOM ROW – Match them over the answer numbers on the opposite page. Repeat the sequence, noticing the numbers around the whole grid, who sits next to each other (think of them as box 'next-door-neighbours').
Look, say, practise, using the 'follow-down' pattern from the top and middle rows.

Visual Memory Test

Use the working grid to cover the practice page you have just been working on, and try placing the cut-out numbers on the grid with the hand you used for counting (see Top Tip). Let's take me as an example: I count on my left hand first, so I will pick up the top row numbers with my left hand, middle row numbers with my right hand and finally bottom row numbers with my left hand again. It takes a bit of practice – and if you're wondering, I'm right-handed.

Lesson Nine – 9 Times Table

	Top Row				
Top Row	9	18	27	36	45
	1	2	3	4	5
Middle Row	54	63	72	81	90
	6	7	8	9	10
Bottom Row	99	108	117	126	135
	11	12	13	14	15

Top Tip!

Here's a fun game for the 9 times table. Take a look at the answer numbers in any box and add them together; what do they add up to? Try another one; does it add up to the same number?

Which is the one box that doesn't add up to this number?

Now you have a fun way to check whether you've got the right number for any answer in the 9 times table... does it add up to 9?

We love the 9 times table! It's a crazy, many-patterned times table. 9 is an odd number, so we can use our old friends the '**odd-even-odd**' and '**jump-down**' patterns. Also we can try out a new one; it's called '**one up, one down**'.

Cut out numbers 9, 18, 27, 36 and 45.

TOP ROW – Match them over the answer numbers on the opposite page. **Look, say, practise**. Now take a look at 'one up, one down' in action. The first digit in each of boxes 2 – 5 goes up in ones (18, 27, 36, 45). The last digit of each goes down in ones (18, 27, 36, 45) – and, as a bonus, these are the digits that will 'jump down' to the bottom row.

Cut out numbers 54, 63, 72, 81 and 90.

MIDDLE ROW – As we match them to the answer numbers on the opposite page, let's see if the 'one up, one down' pattern works on the middle row too. Can you see the same pattern? **Look, say, practise** with the 'one up, one down' pattern until ready to move on to the bottom row.

Cut out numbers 99, 108, 117, 126 and 135.

BOTTOM ROW – Match them to the answer numbers on the opposite page. For the 'one up, one down' pattern on the bottom row, you're looking at the first 2 digits going up and the last 1 digit going down (e.g. in box 12, answer number 108, the 10 has gone up and the 8 has gone down).
Look, say, practise on the bottom row. Don't forget we've also got our other old friend, the 'jump-down' pattern from the top row.

Visual Memory Test

Use the working grid to cover the practice page you have just been working on, and try placing the cut-out numbers on the grid. **Cover, say, practise, practise, practise!**

Revision

Draw and number a blank times table grid. Get someone to ask you a question (e.g. 'what is 5 times 9?') from the 9 times table. Looking at the blank grid, see if the number 'appears' in the box you are looking at.

Now see if you can answer other times table questions with the same blank grid. Each time, find the box and see if the number 'appears'.

Lesson Ten – 10 Times Table

Top Row	10 1	20 2	30 3	40 4	50 5
Middle Row	60 6	70 7	80 8	90 9	100 10
Bottom Row	110 11	120 12	130 13	140 14	150 15

Top Tip!

Draw three boxes, one on top of the other, and number them. I've used the first column as an example; box 1, box 6 and box 11 (see diagram).

10   1
60   6
110   11

Can you still find the answer numbers when they are out of sequence? You can use the 'follow-down' pattern for even times tables or the 'jump-down' pattern for odd times tables. Don't just use the first column, you can try boxes 2, 7 and 12 (second column), boxes 3, 8 and 13 (third column), boxes 4, 9 and 14 (fourth column) or boxes 5, 10 and 15 (fifth column).

We'll keep this one simple. 10 is an even number. Watch those zeros follow down. It's a zero invasion!

Cut out numbers 10, 20, 30, 40 and 50.

TOP ROW – Match them over the answer numbers on the opposite page. **Look, say, practise.**

Cut out numbers 60, 70, 80, 90 and 100.

MIDDLE ROW – Match them over the answer numbers on the opposite page. **Look, say, practise.**

Cut out numbers 110, 120, 130, 140 and 150.

BOTTOM ROW – Match them over the answer numbers on the opposite page. **Look, say, practise.**

At this point you normally bring out your working grid. How about a little change?

As you can probably do this times table spinning on your head (don't panic, I'm not going to suggest that!), how about a game of catch! As you throw the ball in the air shout '1 times 10 is…' and as the ball falls down, shout the answer. To get round that 'no-balls-in-the-house' rule, roll up a pair of your socks. Try some different times tables; like the 7s, remember you made friends with those tricky 7s!

Lesson Eleven – 11 Times Table

Top Row	11 ₁	22 ₂	33 ₃	44 ₄	55 ₅
Middle Row	66 ₆	77 ₇	88 ₈	99 ₉	110 ₁₀
Bottom Row	121 ₁₁	132 ₁₂	143 ₁₃	154 ₁₄	165 ₁₅

Top Tip!

When faced with blank paper (say in a maths test), just getting something down on paper will help to get your maths brain going.

By drawing a grid and beginning to fill in key numbers (e.g.; the answer numbers for boxes 5, 10 and 11) other numbers will start to come into your head. Also try remembering answer numbers for box 8 as it's the middle box in the grid.

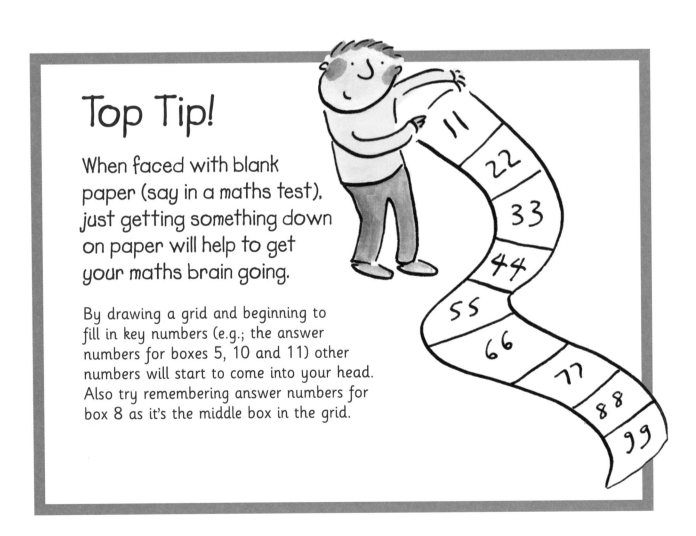

Here's another simple one. Remember 11 is an odd number, and **this times table has its own sequence** (just keep a look out for box 10 onwards).

Cut out numbers 11, 22, 33, 44 and 55.

TOP ROW – Match them over the answer numbers on the top row of the opposite page. **Look, say, practise.**

Cut out numbers 66, 77, 88, 99 and 110.

MIDDLE ROW – Match them over the middle row of the opposite page. **Look, say, practise.**

Cut out numbers 121, 132, 143, 154 and 165.

BOTTOM ROW – Match them over the bottom row using the 'jump-down' pattern from the top row. **Look, say, practise.**

Visual Memory Test

Use the working grid to cover the practice page you have just been working on, and try placing the cut-out numbers on the grid.

If you look carefully at the bottom row, as well as the **'jump-down'** pattern, the first 2 digits of the answer numbers also go up in a sequence (12, 13, 14, 15, 16).

121	132	143	154	165
11	12	13	14	15

Cover, say, practise until you feel confident with this times table.

Revision
Practise doodling grids and filling in key memory numbers (see Top Tip) for all the times tables you've done so far.

Lesson Twelve – 12 Times Table

Top Row	12	24	36	48	60
	1	2	3	4	5
Middle Row	72	84	96	108	120
		7	8	9	10
Bottom Row	132	144	156	168	180
	11	12	13	14	15

Top Tip!

You've worked so hard and learned all the times tables, so give yourself a break just this once!

But should you find yourself bored one rainy day, get a working grid, pick a number between 12 and 98 and have a go at writing your own times table grid, just like dear old Victorius of Aquitaine did. I chose 97, and it did follow the '**jump-down**' and '**odd-even-odd**' patterns. It became strangely calming, just adding the same number over and over again!

Last one! 12 is an even number, therefore **it's even numbers all the way**. Although the numbers get to be quite big, we've seen most of them before (up to box 11).

This is the sixth time we've seen the number 24!

Cut out numbers 12, 24, 36, 48 and 60

TOP ROW – Match them over the answer numbers on the top row of the opposite page. **Look, say, practise.**

Cut out numbers 72, 84, 96, 108 and 120.

MIDDLE ROW – Match them over the answer numbers on the opposite page using the 'follow-down' pattern from the top row. (Watch out for boxes 9 and 10, they are already in the hundreds!) **Look, say, practise.**

Cut out numbers 132, 144, 156, 168 and 180.

BOTTOM ROW – Match them over the answer numbers on the bottom row. (The 'follow-down' pattern will be useful for these big numbers.) **Look, say, practise.**

Visual Memory Test

Using the working grid, cover the practice page you have just been working on. Turn the cut-out answer numbers over, shuffle them around and then place them on the grid. **Cover, say, practise** until you feel confident with this times table.

Revision

You can prepare for oral testing (saying questions and answers out loud, by picturing a grid in your mind and using your recall of key answers (boxes 5, 10, 15 and box 8) to work your way backwards or forwards and find the answer number you're looking for. Use your hand counting as a backup strategy!

Times Table Activities

Random Number Game

Test your memory by seeing if you can guess the times table from just a few numbers in a times table grid.

1	**6** 2	3	4	5
6	7	8	9	10
11	12	**39** 13	14	15

1	2	**15** 3	4	5
6	7	8	9	10
11	**60** 12	13	14	15

1	2	3	4	5
	28			
6	7	8	9	10
				60
11	12	13	14	15

1	2	3	4	5
		16		
6	7	8	9	10
			28	
11	12	13	14	15

1	2	3	4	5
6	**49** 7	8	9	10
11	12	13	14	15

1	**24** 2	3	4	5
6	7	8	9	10
11	12	13	14	15

1	2	**24** 3	4	5
6	7	**64** 8	9	10
11	12	13	14	15

Grid 1

1	2	3	4	5
24				
6	7	8	9	10
11	12	13	14	15

Grid 2

			24	
1	2	3	4	5
6	7	8	9	10
11	12	13	14	15

Grid 3

	24			
1	2	3	4	5
			108	
6	7	8	9	10
11	12	13	14	15

1	2	3	4	5
6	7	8	9	10 **110**
11	12	13	14	15

	18			
1	2	3	4	5
6	7	8	9	10
11	**108** 12	13	14	15

Times Table Bingo

This can be played with one caller and any number of players, or teams of players.

You will need:

- A bingo sheet with 3 blank times table grids (from the cut-out section of this book).

- A caller sheet with all completed times table grids.

Bingo Player Card

Bingo Caller Card

Two Times Table

2	4	6	8	10
1	2	3	4	5
12	14	16	18	20
6	7	8	9	10
22	24	26	28	30
11	12	13	14	15

Rules of the game:

- Each player or team has a sheet with three blank times table grids.

BINGO!

- The caller gives three box 1 answer numbers, players fill in their box 1s. (The caller needs to decide which of the three times table grids is going to be completed.)

- The caller calls out random answer numbers from any of the three selected times tables.

- The players or teams fill in as many boxes as they can with each called number.

- The first player or team to complete a full times table grid shouts out 'Bingo!'

Only play the levels that everyone is confident with – so if that means just doing the top and middle rows, then that's fine. The idea is to see how confident you are with recalling the numbers.

To change the game slightly, instead of calling out the answer numbers, the caller could call out times table questions such as '5 times 5 is …?' or '8 times 7 is …?'.

This will encourage memory recall because the grid is in front of the players.

Being able to see where the answer should go will hopefully help take the panic out of times table tests!

Cut-out numbers can be used if writing numbers is tricky, so that the numbers themselves can be concentrated on.

Let's Learn Division!

Our times table grids can also help us to see the links between division and multiplication; all we need to do is read the grid in a slightly different way.

If the question is 60 ÷ 4 = ? we are being asked how many times 60 will divide into 4 groups.

The smallest number in a division question tells which times table grid to use.

So which one do we need? ... yes, the 4 times table grid.

Top Row	4 1	8 2	12 3	16 4	20 5
Middle Row	24 6	28 7	32 8	36 9	40 10
Bottom Row	44 11	48 12	52 13	56 14	60 15

Where can we see the number 60? Which box it is in?

For division, the box number will be the answer.
60 is in box 15, so the answer to the question is 15.

60 ÷ 4 = 15

Another example: 32 ÷ 4 = ?

Where can we see the number 32? Which box it is in?

32 is in box 8, so the answer to the question is 8.

32 ÷ 4 = 8

Use this blank times table grid and your visual memory to 'drop in' the numbers you need for each of the following division questions.

Top Row				
1	2	3	4	5
Middle Row				
6	7	8	9	10
Bottom Row				
11	12	13	14	15

$28 \div 2 =$

(in the 2 times table grid, which box do you 'see' the number 28 in?)

$18 \div 3 =$

(in the 3 times table grid, which box do you 'see' the number 18 in?)

$40 \div 5 =$

(in the 5 times table grid, which box do you 'see' the number 40 in?)

$54 \div 6 =$

(in the 6 times table grid, which box do you 'see' the number 54 in?)

$84 \div 7 =$

(in the 7 times table grid, which box do you 'see' the number 84 in?)

$112 \div 8 =$

(in the 8 times table grid, which box do you 'see' the number 112 in?)

$27 \div 9 =$

(in the 9 times table grid, which box do you 'see' the number 27 in)

Cards

odd	odd	odd	odd	odd	odd
odd	odd	odd	odd	odd	odd
odd	odd	odd	even	even	even
even	even	even	even	even	even
even	even	even	even	even	even

Lesson Two 2 Times Table	2	4	6
8	10	12	14
16	18	20	22
24	26	28	30

odds & evens   odds & evens   odds & evens   odds & evens   odds & evens   odds & evens

odds & evens   odds & evens   odds & evens   odds & evens   odds & evens   odds & evens

odds & evens   odds & evens   odds & evens   odds & evens   odds & evens   odds & evens

odds & evens   odds & evens   odds & evens   odds & evens   odds & evens   odds & evens

odds & evens   odds & evens   odds & evens   odds & evens   odds & evens   odds & evens

2 Times Table   **2** Times Table   **2** Times Table   **2** Times Table

2 Times Table   **2** Times Table   **2** Times Table   **2** Times Table

2 Times Table   **2** Times Table   **2** Times Table   **2** Times Table

2 Times Table   **2** Times Table   **2** Times Table   **2** Times Table

	3	6	9
Lesson Three 3 Times Table			
12	15	18	21
24	27	30	33
36	39	42	45
Lesson Four 4 Times Table	4	8	12
16	20	24	28
32	36	40	44
48	52	56	60

3 Times Table	**3** Times Table	**3** Times Table	**3** Times Table
3 Times Table	**3** Times Table	**3** Times Table	**3** Times Table
3 Times Table	**3** Times Table	**3** Times Table	**3** Times Table
3 Times Table	**3** Times Table	**3** Times Table	**3** Times Table
4 Times Table	**4** Times Table	**4** Times Table	**4** Times Table
4 Times Table	**4** Times Table	**4** Times Table	**4** Times Table
4 Times Table	**4** Times Table	**4** Times Table	**4** Times Table
4 Times Table	**4** Times Table	**4** Times Table	**4** Times Table

Lesson Five **5 Times Table**	5	10	15
20	25	30	35
40	45	50	55
60	65	70	75
Lesson Six **6 Times Table**	6	12	18
24	30	36	42
48	54	60	66
72	78	84	90

5
Times Table

5
Times Table

5
Times Table

5
Times Table

5
Times Table

5
Times Table

5
Times Table

5
Times Table

5
Times Table

5
Times Table

5
Times Table

5
Times Table

5
Times Table

5
Times Table

5
Times Table

5
Times Table

6
Times Table

6
Times Table

6
Times Table

6
Times Table

6
Times Table

6
Times Table

6
Times Table

6
Times Table

6
Times Table

6
Times Table

6
Times Table

6
Times Table

6
Times Table

6
Times Table

6
Times Table

6
Times Table

Lesson Seven 7 Times Table	7	14	21
28	35	42	49
56	63	70	77
84	91	98	105
Lesson Eight 8 Times Table	8	16	24
32	40	48	56
64	72	80	88
96	104	112	120

7
Times Table

7
Times Table

7
Times Table

7
Times Table

7
Times Table

7
Times Table

7
Times Table

7
Times Table

7
Times Table

7
Times Table

7
Times Table

7
Times Table

7
Times Table

7
Times Table

7
Times Table

7
Times Table

8
Times Table

8
Times Table

8
Times Table

8
Times Table

8
Times Table

8
Times Table

8
Times Table

8
Times Table

8
Times Table

8
Times Table

8
Times Table

8
Times Table

8
Times Table

8
Times Table

8
Times Table

8
Times Table

Lesson Nine **9 Times Table**	9	18	27
36	45	54	63
72	81	90	99
108	117	126	135
Lesson Ten **10 Times Table**	10	20	30
40	50	60	70
80	90	100	110
120	130	140	150

9 Times Table

9 Times Table

9 Times Table

9 Times Table

9 Times Table

9 Times Table

9 Times Table

9 Times Table

9 Times Table

9 Times Table

9 Times Table

9 Times Table

9 Times Table

9 Times Table

9 Times Table

9 Times Table

10 Times Table

10 Times Table

10 Times Table

10 Times Table

10 Times Table

10 Times Table

10 Times Table

10 Times Table

10 Times Table

10 Times Table

10 Times Table

10 Times Table

10 Times Table

10 Times Table

10 Times Table

10 Times Table

Lesson Eleven **11 Times Table**	11	22	33
44	55	66	77
88	99	110	121
132	143	154	165
Lesson Twelve **12 Times Table**	12	24	36
48	60	72	84
96	108	120	132
144	156	168	180

11
Times Table

11
Times Table

11
Times Table

11
Times Table

11
Times Table

11
Times Table

11
Times Table

11
Times Table

11
Times Table

11
Times Table

11
Times Table

11
Times Table

11
Times Table

11
Times Table

11
Times Table

11
Times Table

12
Times Table

12
Times Table

12
Times Table

12
Times Table

12
Times Table

12
Times Table

12
Times Table

12
Times Table

12
Times Table

12
Times Table

12
Times Table

12
Times Table

12
Times Table

12
Times Table

12
Times Table

12
Times Table

Bingo Caller Cards

Bingo Caller Card

2
Times
Table

2 _1_	4 _2_	6 _3_	8 _4_	10 _5_
12 _6_	14 _7_	16 _8_	18 _9_	20 _10_
22 _11_	24 _12_	26 _13_	28 _14_	30 _15_

Bingo Caller Card

3
Times
Table

3 _1_	6 _2_	9 _3_	12 _4_	15 _5_
18 _6_	21 _7_	24 _8_	27 _9_	30 _10_
33 _11_	36 _12_	39 _13_	42 _14_	45 _15_

2 Times Table

3 Times Table

Bingo Caller Card

4
Times
Table

4 ₁	8 ₂	12 ₃	16 ₄	20 ₅
24 ₆	28 ₇	32 ₈	36 ₉	40 ₁₀
44 ₁₁	48 ₁₂	52 ₁₃	56 ₁₄	60 ₁₅

Bingo Caller Card

5
Times
Table

5 ₁	10 ₂	15 ₃	20 ₄	25 ₅
30 ₆	35 ₇	40 ₈	45 ₉	50 ₁₀
55 ₁₁	60 ₁₂	65 ₁₃	70 ₁₄	75 ₁₅

Bingo Caller Card

6
Times
Table

6 ₁	12 ₂	18 ₃	24 ₄	30 ₅
36 ₆	42 ₇	48 ₈	54 ₉	60 ₁₀
66 ₁₁	72 ₁₂	78 ₁₃	84 ₁₄	90 ₁₅

Bingo Caller Card

4 Times Table

Bingo Caller Card

5 Times Table

Bingo Caller Card

6 Times Table

7
Times
Table

7 1	14 2	21 3	28 4	35 5
42 6	49 7	56 8	63 9	70 10
77 11	84 12	91 13	98 14	105 15

8
Times
Table

8 1	16 2	24 3	32 4	40 5
48 6	56 7	64 8	72 9	80 10
88 11	96 12	104 13	112 14	120 15

9
Times
Table

9 1	18 2	27 3	36 4	45 5
54 6	63 7	72 8	81 9	90 10
99 11	108 12	117 13	126 14	135 15

7 Times Table

8 Times Table

9 Times Table

10 Times Table

10 _1_	20 _2_	30 _3_	40 _4_	50 _5_
60 _6_	70 _7_	80 _8_	90 _9_	100 _10_
110 _11_	120 _12_	130 _13_	140 _14_	150 _15_

11 Times Table

11 _1_	22 _2_	33 _3_	44 _4_	55 _5_
66 _6_	77 _7_	88 _8_	99 _9_	110 _10_
121 _11_	132 _12_	143 _13_	154 _14_	165 _15_

12 Times Table

12 _1_	24 _2_	36 _3_	48 _4_	60 _5_
72 _6_	84 _7_	96 _8_	108 _9_	120 _10_
136 _11_	144 _12_	156 _13_	168 _14_	180 _15_

Bingo Caller Card
10 Times Table

Bingo Caller Card
11 Times Table

Bingo Caller Card
12 Times Table

Bingo Player Card

1	2	3	4	5
6	7	8	9	10
11	12	13	14	15

Bingo Player Card

1	2	3	4	5
6	7	8	9	10
11	12	13	14	15

Bingo Player Card

1	2	3	4	5
6	7	8	9	10
11	12	13	14	15

1	2	3	4	5
6	7	8	9	10
11	12	13	14	15

1	2	3	4	5
6	7	8	9	10
11	12	13	14	15

1	2	3	4	5
6	7	8	9	10
11	12	13	14	15

1	2	3	4	5
6	7	8	9	10
11	12	13	14	15

1	2	3	4	5
6	7	8	9	10
11	12	13	14	15

1	2	3	4	5
6	7	8	9	10
11	12	13	14	15

Bingo Player Card

1	6	11
2	7	12
3	8	13
4	9	14
5	10	15

1	6	11
2	7	12
3	8	13
4	9	14
5	10	15

1	6	11
2	7	12
3	8	13
4	9	14
5	10	15

Bingo Player Card

1	6	11
2	7	12
3	8	13
4	9	14
5	10	15

1	6	11
2	7	12
3	8	13
4	9	14
5	10	15

1	6	11
2	7	12
3	8	13
4	9	14
5	10	15

Bingo Player Card

1	6	11
2	7	12
3	8	13
4	9	14
5	10	15

1	6	11
2	7	12
3	8	13
4	9	14
5	10	15

1	6	11
2	7	12
3	8	13
4	9	14
5	10	15

Bingo Player Card

A page of nine blank Bingo Player Cards. Each card is a 3×5 grid with cells numbered 1 through 15.

Bingo Player Card

5	4	3	2	1
10	9	8	7	6
15	14	13	12	11

5	4	3	2	1
10	9	8	7	6
15	14	13	12	11

5	4	3	2	1
10	9	8	7	6
15	14	13	12	11

Bingo Player Card

5	4	3	2	1
10	9	8	7	6
15	14	13	12	11

5	4	3	2	1
10	9	8	7	6
15	14	13	12	11

5	4	3	2	1
10	9	8	7	6
15	14	13	12	11

Bingo Player Card

5	4	3	2	1
10	9	8	7	6
15	14	13	12	11

5	4	3	2	1
10	9	8	7	6
15	14	13	12	11

5	4	3	2	1
10	9	8	7	6
15	14	13	12	11

Bingo Player Card

1	6	11
2	7	12
3	8	13
4	9	14
5	10	15

1	6	11
2	7	12
3	8	13
4	9	14
5	10	15

1	6	11
2	7	12
3	8	13
4	9	14
5	10	15

Bingo Player Card

1	6	11
2	7	12
3	8	13
4	9	14
5	10	15

1	6	11
2	7	12
3	8	13
4	9	14
5	10	15

1	6	11
2	7	12
3	8	13
4	9	14
5	10	15

Bingo Player Card

1	6	11
2	7	12
3	8	13
4	9	14
5	10	15

1	6	11
2	7	12
3	8	13
4	9	14
5	10	15

1	6	11
2	7	12
3	8	13
4	9	14
5	10	15

Bingo Player Card

1	2	3	4	5
6	7	8	9	10
11	12	13	14	15

1	2	3	4	5
6	7	8	9	10
11	12	13	14	15

1	2	3	4	5
6	7	8	9	10
11	12	13	14	15

Bingo Player Card

1	2	3	4	5
6	7	8	9	10
11	12	13	14	15

1	2	3	4	5
6	7	8	9	10
11	12	13	14	15

1	2	3	4	5
6	7	8	9	10
11	12	13	14	15

Bingo Player Card

1	2	3	4	5
6	7	8	9	10
11	12	13	14	15

1	2	3	4	5
6	7	8	9	10
11	12	13	14	15

1	2	3	4	5
6	7	8	9	10
11	12	13	14	15

Bingo Player Card

1	6	11
2	7	12
3	8	13
4	9	14
5	10	15

Bingo Player Card

1	6	11
2	7	12
3	8	13
4	9	14
5	10	15

Bingo Player Card

1	6	11
2	7	12
3	8	13
4	9	14
5	10	15

Bingo Player Card

1	6	11
2	7	12
3	8	13
4	9	14
5	10	15

Bingo Player Card

1	6	11
2	7	12
3	8	13
4	9	14
5	10	15

Bingo Player Card

1	6	11
2	7	12
3	8	13
4	9	14
5	10	15

Bingo Player Card

1	6	11
2	7	12
3	8	13
4	9	14
5	10	15

Bingo Player Card

1	6	11
2	7	12
3	8	13
4	9	14
5	10	15

Bingo Player Card

1	6	11
2	7	12
3	8	13
4	9	14
5	10	15

Notes

Notes

A word from Penny Topsom

I approached Ragged Bears with my multiplication idea, after having read and worked through the fabulous *Dyslexia Rules!* by Mary Manning-Thomas. The foreword written by Henrietta Stickland struck a chord with me. At the time I also had a child struggling to find a practical, uncomplicated approach that would help with his reading and spelling. I found the book gave us just what we were looking for: fun, visual aids and lots of repetition practice, a learning approach that was easy to understand and follow.

I thought Ragged Bears might be interested in creating a 'sister-book' for children struggling with maths and particularly multiplication. Using a small times table grid they can learn a few simple multiplication rules which can then be used to learn any times table. This visual way of working builds up a solid base for children to learn from - they can see the numbers arranging themselves into patterns. I hope that *Multiplication Rules!* will provide some fun and be a useful way of restoring people's confidence in their natural mathematical abilities.

Acknowledgements

This book would not have been possible if my boys hadn't questioned the very notion of times table numbers and pushed my imagination to the max - thank you Sonny, Harvey and Cozmo. To Jonathan, who had to sit listening to me go on and on about the patterns - a huge thank you. To Julia Clark, Judith Wales, and all the teachers and staff at Horniman Primary School, for welcoming me into the school to work with the children and for all their encouraging words. A big "Head Shout" to Alex, Louis, Tilly, Oscar, Fenn, Yinka, Zac and Sadie. For guiding me through the publishing process with encouragement and support, many thanks to Henrietta, Elinor and Martin. And lastly, in memory of Neil Radford who could do maths – thank you.

Penny Topsom works with children with special educational needs at the Horniman School in Forest Hill, South-east London. She is married with three boys aged 4, 8 and 10.

Also from Ragged Bears Publishing

Dyslexia Rules!

An Activity Book of basic lessons for severe reading and spelling disability

Mary Manning-Thomas

This book is made of word lists and exercises that have helped children over a period of many years. The lesson plans are easy and fun to use and with constant repetition progress will be made very rapidly.

Whether used in the home, school or learning support unit, this book will help give dyslexics strong and simple tools to help find their way through the complexities of the English language.

Appropriate for year 5 upwards (from approximately 10 year – adult).

ISBN 978-1-85714-372-0

Available from Ragged Bears Publishing Ltd
Tel: 01963 34300 orders@raggedbears.co.uk

Multiplication Rules!

'It has been really exciting to see how children have responded to the new times table format. It is such a clever idea. By simply rearranging the dimensions of the table, very clear visual patterns emerge that reveal the pattern and order of numbers. This has resulted in children not just remembering their tables but also in developing a deeper understanding of mathematics.'

JULIA CLARK
HEADTEACHER, HORNIMAN PRIMARY SCHOOL